# WHERE'S THE NARWHAL?

ORCHARD

ORCHARD BOOKS

First published in Great Britain in 2019 by The Watts Publishing Group

1 3 5 7 9 10 8 6 4 2

© 2019 The Watts Publishing Group Limited

Illustrations by Dynamo Limited

Additional images © Shutterstock

A CIP catalogue record for this book is available from the British Library

ISBN 978 1 40835 946 4

Printed and bound in China

MIX
Paper from
responsible sources
FSC
www.fsc.org
FSC® C104740

Orchard Books
An imprint of Hachette Children's Group
Part of The Watts Publishing Group Limited
Carmelite House
50 Victoria Embankment
London EC4Y 0DZ

An Hachette UK Company
www.hachette.co.uk

# WHERE'S THE NARWHAL?

# MEET THE UNICORNS OF THE SEA!

Narwhals are a type of whale with a special tusk. The tusk is actually a big tooth and can grow up to three metres long! Narwhals usually live in the Arctic, feeding on fish, squid and shrimp, but the special narwhals in this book are going on an adventure!

Can you spot the family as they travel round the world?

The answers are at the back of the book, along with some extra things to look out for!

## NIALL

Niall looks out for his two younger siblings. He's a natural worrier so the thought of travelling the world is a little scary!

## NICOLA

Nicola loves having fun and playing pranks on her family. She is always making mischief wherever she goes!

## NOAH

Noah is the baby of the narwhal family and the most excited about their new adventure! He loves exploring his Arctic home but can't wait to travel the world.

# ROBBIE RAINBOW

Robbie is a very special rainbow narwhal! Can you spot Robbie in one of the scenes?

# NIGEL

The dad of the family, Nigel has organised this trip of a lifetime! He has always wanted to visit a tropical island and now is his chance!

# NATALIE

Natalie is eager to share lots of new experiences with her family. She has dreamt of the world outside the Arctic since she was young.

# NANCY

Nancy is the oldest and wisest of the narwhals. She has seen many things in her life, but is about to have lots of new adventures!

SEASIDE

First stop is the beach! The narwhals can't wait to relax in the sun. It's very different to the Arctic!

PARTY TIME

The narwhals have travelled back to the cold, where animals from the Arctic and Antarctic have all gathered for a special party!

# PENGUIN PARADE

The narwhals have got caught up in a penguin parade!

Odd one out!

Can you spot the penguin that looks different to the rest?

# PIER

Down at the town pier, the narwhals are looking forward to a day out. Fish and chips, anyone?

# CITY CENTRE

The city centre is very busy but the narwhals want to do some shopping. There aren't many shops in the Arctic!

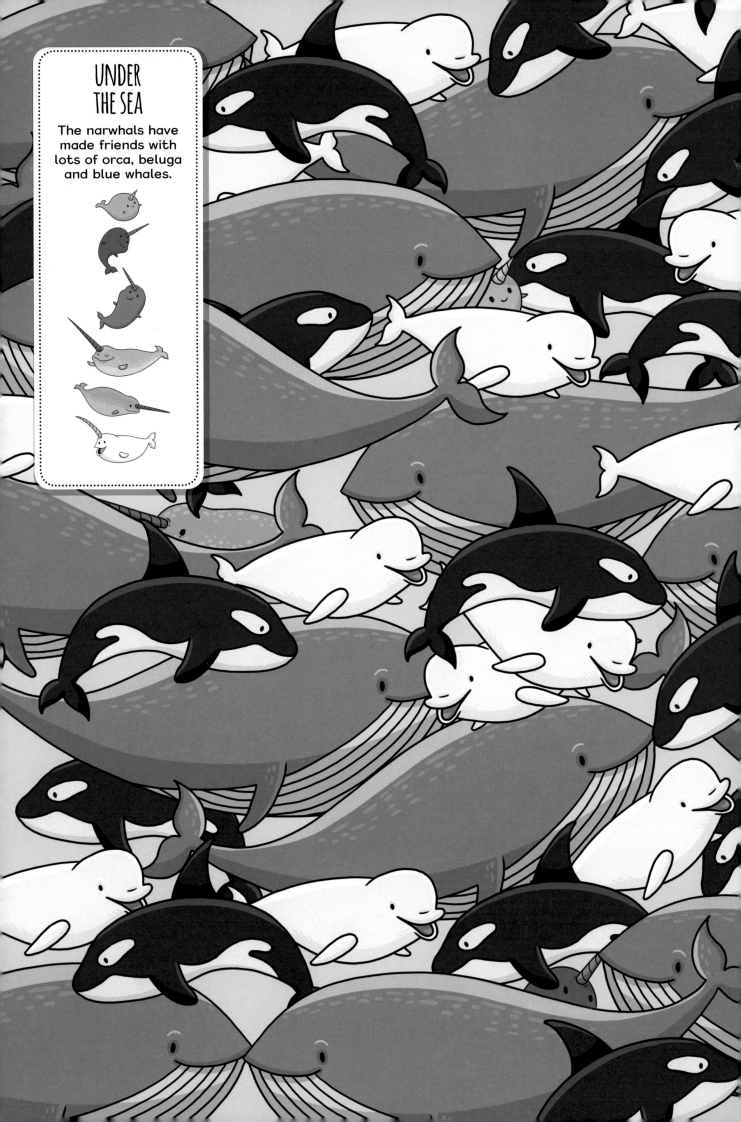

# UNDER THE SEA

The narwhals have made friends with lots of orca, beluga and blue whales.

# MUSEUM

The museum is a great place to learn about the world. The narwhals are particularly excited to see the dinosaur skeletons!

# WATER PARK

After all their travelling, the narwhals are relaxing at the water park. They love the slides!

# UNICORN GATHERING

The unicorns of the sea have met lots of magical unicorns!

Odd one out!

Can you spot the unicorn that looks different to the rest?

# WHITE WATER RAFTING

Time for some thrills! The narwhals are ready for the rapids and white water rafting.

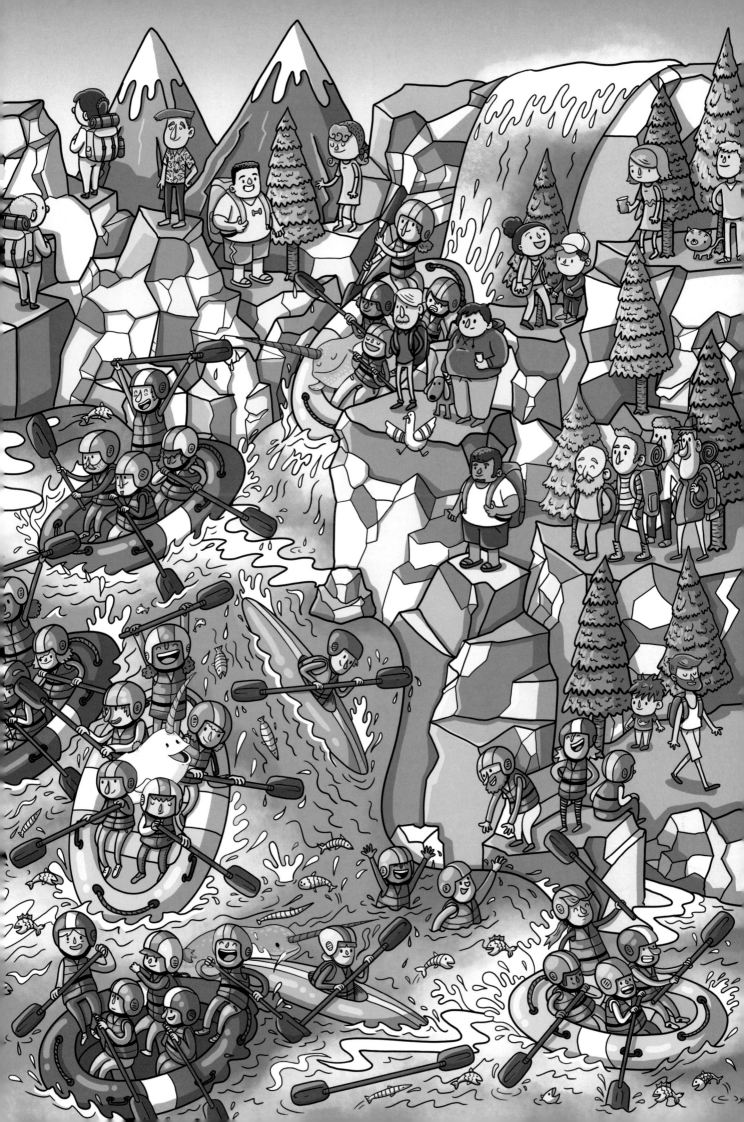

# THEME PARK

Niall is a bit scared of the rides but Nicola can't wait to go on the big rollercoaster!

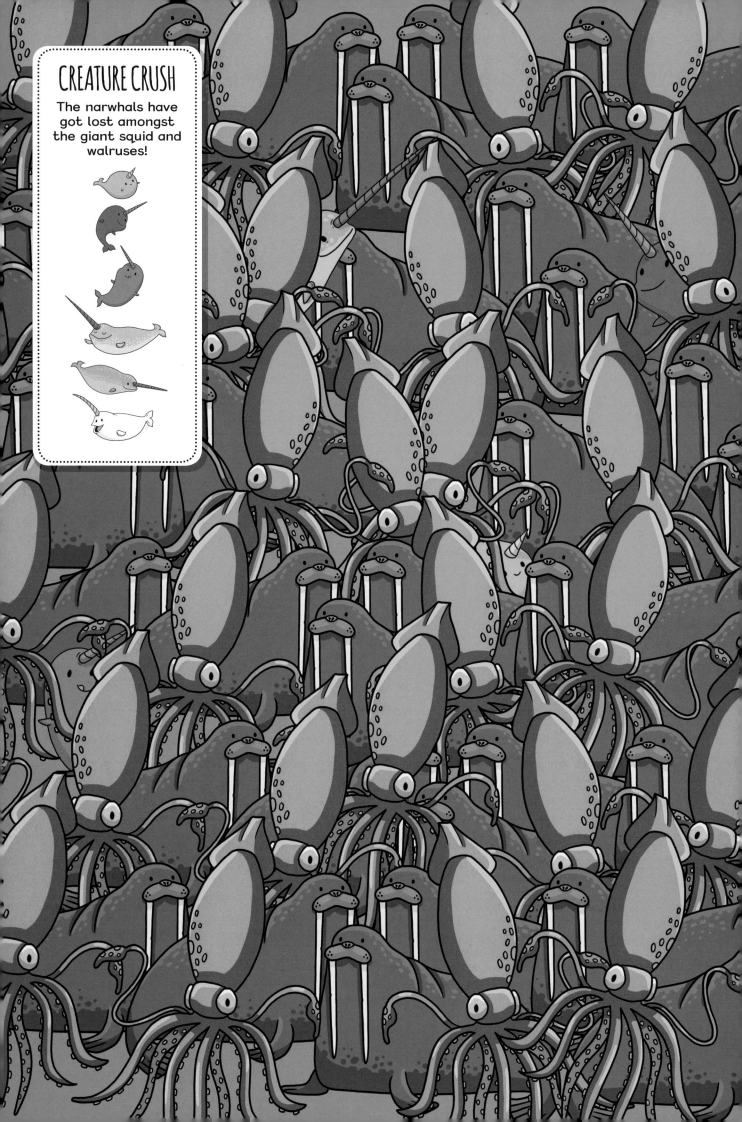

CREATURE CRUSH

The narwhals have
got lost amongst
the giant squid and
walruses!

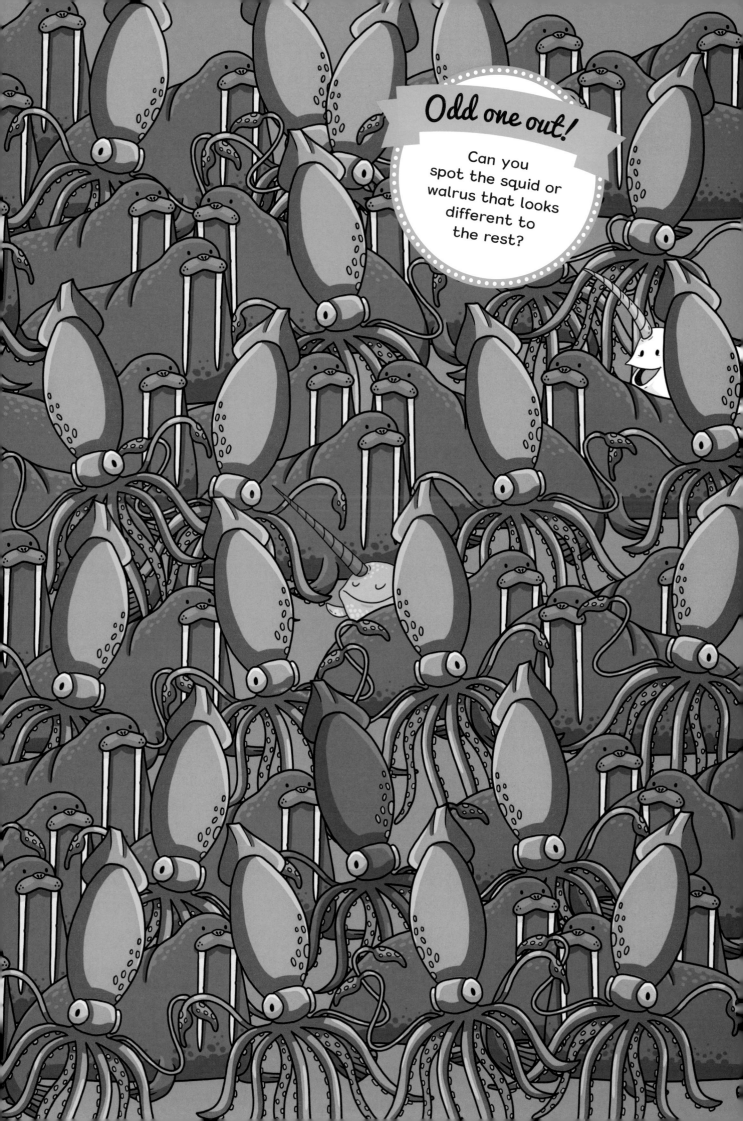

Odd one out!

Can you spot the squid or walrus that looks different to the rest?

## SAFARI

The family has travelled all the way to Africa to go on safari. There are so many new animals to see!

## PENGUIN PARADE

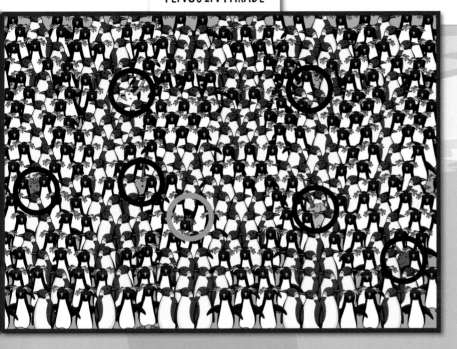

## PIER

Two boys using binoculars ☐

A seagull eating a chip ☐

A baby ☐

A boy eating candy floss ☐

A man with a skull on his cap ☐

A girl with a fish-shaped balloon ☐

A man reading a newspaper ☐

A woman eating fish and chips ☐

A man with a moustache, wearing a tie ☐

A seagull in a pirate hat ☐

# CITY CENTRE

A teddy bear ☐

A man with a fancy moustache ☐

A man reading a newspaper ☐

A woman wearing a pink hat ☐

A man riding a penny-farthing ☐

A dog looking out of a window ☐

A boy on a scooter ☐

A tabby cat ☐

A man wearing a Hawaiian shirt ☐

A woman looking in a mirror ☐

## UNDER THE SEA

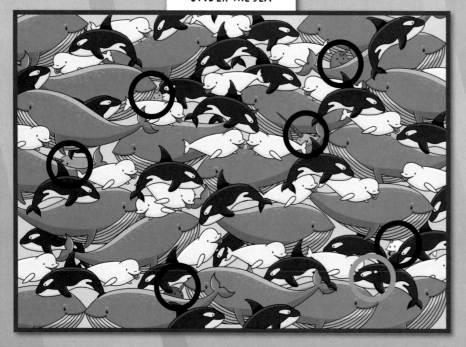

## MUSEUM

A girl wearing orange headphones ☐

A boy with a spider on his T-shirt ☐

A girl with a heart on her T-shirt ☐

A boy with an eye patch ☐

A man with stripy trousers ☐

A man with a pen behind his ear ☐

A boy with a dinosaur on his T-shirt ☐

A picture of an elephant ☐

A boy wearing a bow tie ☐

A man wearing sunglasses ☐

## WATER PARK

A slice of watermelon ☐

A man having a shower ☐

A boy running by the pool ☐

An alligator inflatable ☐

Someone wearing flippers ☐

An orange ball ☐

Someone enjoying the hot tub ☐

A lifeguard ☐

Someone climbing out of the pool ☐

Four starfish inflatables ☐

## UNICORN GATHERING

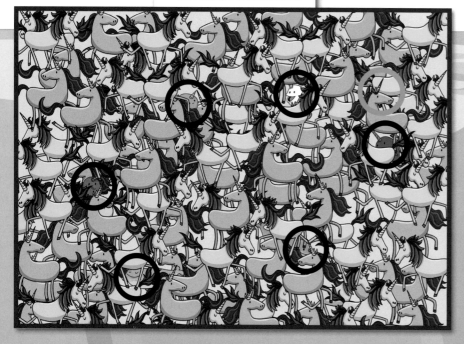

## WHITE WATER RAFTING

- A man eating a sandwich ☐
- Two people in the water ☐
- A woman wearing a bandana ☐
- A man with walking sticks ☐
- A man with a long white beard ☐
- Someone wearing green sandals ☐
- A dog next to a ball ☐
- A man with a backwards cap ☐
- A woman holding a red cup ☐
- A man with binoculars ☐

# AIRPORT

It's time to go home so the narwhals have come to the airport for their flight. They can't wait to go on their next adventure!

# Answers

Now try and find these extra items in every scene!

## SEASIDE

A boy buried in sand ☐

A dog digging a hole ☐

A boy eating a hot dog ☐

A woman with a heart on her hat ☐

A man reading a map ☐

A rhino inflatable ☐

A woman knitting ☐

Two children playing with a bat and ball ☐

A man with a green mohawk ☐

A man holding two ice creams ☐

## PARTY TIME

An Arctic fox with armbands ☐

A penguin on a polar bear ☐

A snowman with a top hat ☐

A bucket filled with fish ☐

A penguin jumping off a diving board ☐

An Arctic hare in an inflatable ring ☐

A woman in a stripy scarf ☐

A polar bear eating a fish ☐

A man wearing ski goggles ☐

An Arctic fox carrying a bone ☐

## THEME PARK

Someone scared of the teacups ☐

A clown ☐

A man on a ride wearing a hat ☐

A lion balloon ☐

A girl dressed as a superhero ☐

A man eating a hot dog ☐

A Frankenstein's monster ☐

A girl reading by the ferris wheel ☐

An octopus ☐

A mummy ☐

## CREATURE CRUSH

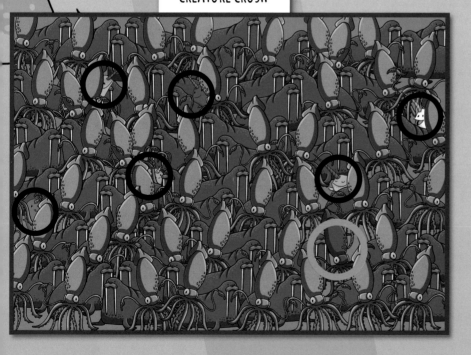

## SAFARI

A lion sitting on a rock ☐

Two men taking pictures ☐

A hungry hippo ☐

A monkey holding a banana ☐

Two sad frogs ☐

A pair of dice ☐

Spotlights ☐

A boy enjoying the safari ☐

A monkey climbing a tree ☐

A lion having a bath ☐

## AIRPORT

A man pointing at the escalator ☐

A man wearing a white vest ☐

A girl in pink sitting on a suitcase ☐

A boy with lightning on his T-shirt ☐

A man wearing a straw hat ☐

A muffin ☐

A man in a white shirt and black tie ☐

A man bored waiting for security ☐

A woman with blue hair ☐

A boy crying ☐